1 Buttercup

2 Tiger

3 Macaroni

Coco

10 Buster

One Guinea Pig Is Not Enough

5 Pigwiggin

9 Peaches

8 Floradora

7 Plato

6 Tex

One Guinea Pig

SCHOLASTIC INC.
New York Toronto London Auckland Sydney
Mexico City New Delhi Hong Kong

Is Not Enough

• Kate Duke •

ISBN 0-590-98720-8

Copyright © 1998 by Kate Duke.
All rights reserved.
Published by Scholastic Inc., 555 Broadway, New York, NY 10012,
by arrangement with Dutton Children's Books, a division of Penguin Putnam, Inc.
SCHOLASTIC and associated logos are trademarks and/or registered
trademarks of Scholastic Inc.

12 11 10 9 8 7 6 5 4 3 2 1   9/9 0 1 2 3 4/0

Printed in the U.S.A.   14

First Scholastic printing, January 1999

The artwork was rendered in acrylic, watercolor, pencil,
colored pencil, and colored inks.
Designed by Amy Berniker

To Sidney

One guinea pig
is not enough.

One guinea pig is a lonely guinea pig.

One lonely guinea pig

plus one other lonely guinea pig

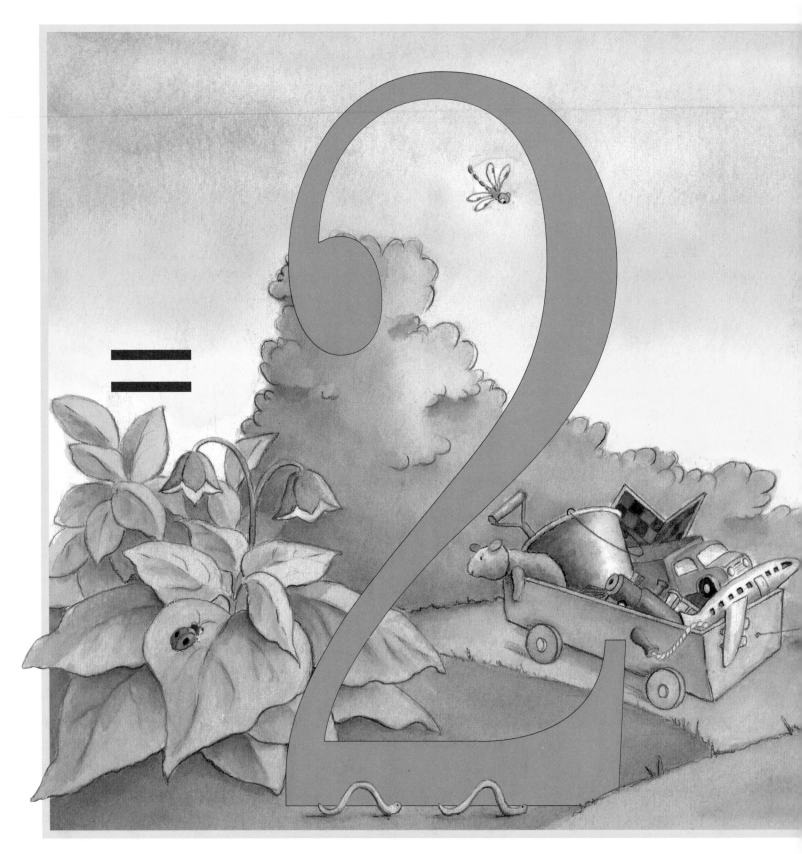

make two

smiling guinea pigs.

1+1=2

Two smiling guinea pigs

plus one silly guinea pig

make three

giggling guinea pigs.

2+1=3

Three giggling guinea pigs

plus one singing guinea pig

make four

dancing guinea pigs.

3+1=4

Four dancing guinea pigs

plus one jumping guinea pig

make five

flying guinea pigs.

4+1=5

Five flying guinea pigs

plus one proud guinea pig

make six

sorry guinea pigs.

5+1=6

Six sorry guinea pigs

plus one smart guinea pig

make seven

helpful guinea pigs.

6+1=7

Seven helpful guinea pigs

plus one hungry guinea pig

make eight

picnicking guinea pigs.

7+1=8

Eight picnicking guinea pigs

plus one sneaky guinea pig

make nine

fighting guinea pigs.

$8+1=9$

Nine fighting guinea pigs

plus one big guinea pig

make ten

good guinea pigs.

9+1=10

Ten good guinea pigs

plus ten mom or dad guinea pigs

make twenty

hugging guinea pigs—

$10+10=20$

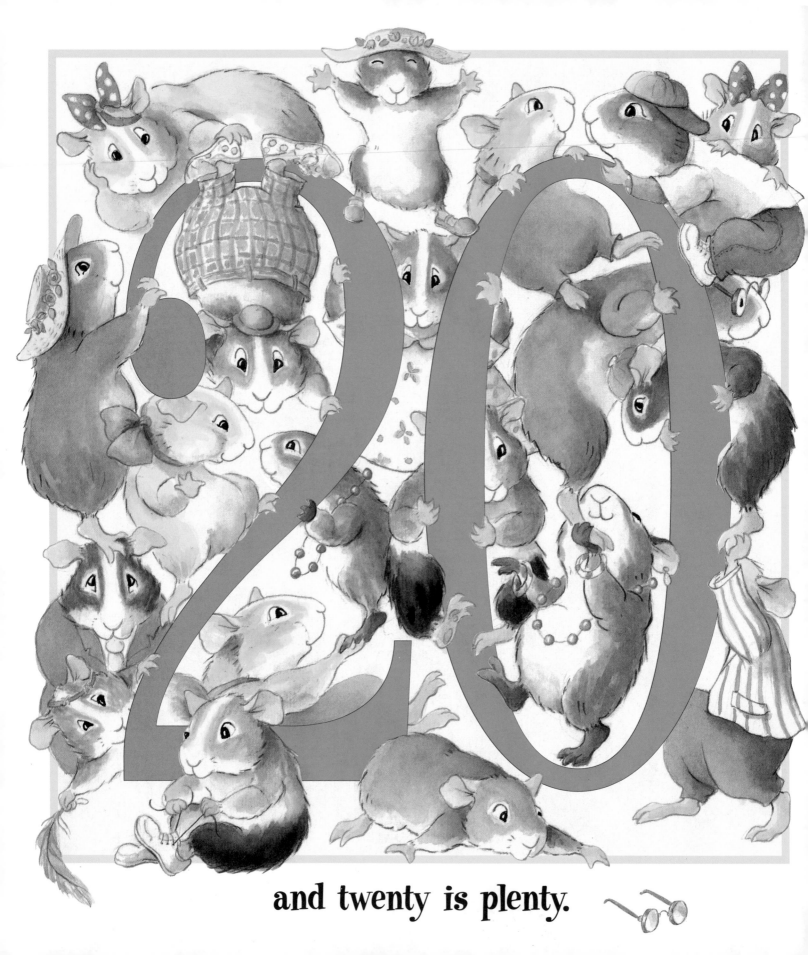

and twenty is plenty.